retu_____ the ___

GOAL

Dee Phillips

D0609966

Evans

First published in 2009
by Evans Brothers Limited
2A Portman Mansions
Chiltern Street
London W1U 6NR
UK

Printed in Dubai

All rights reserved. No part of this publication may be reproduced, stored in a retrieval system, or transmitted, in any form, or by any means, electronic, mechanical, photocopying, or otherwise, without prior permission of Evans Brothers Limited.

British Library Cataloguing in Publication Data
Phillips, Dee.
      Goal. -- (Right now)
      1. Graphic novels. 2. Young adult fiction.
      I. Title II. Series
      741.5-dc22
      ISBN-13: 9780237539528

Developed & Created by Ruby Tuesday Books Ltd

Project Director – Ruth Owen
Head of Design – Elaine Wilkinson
Designer – Alix Wood
Editor – Frances Ridley
Consultant – Lorraine Petersen, Chief Executive of NASEN
© Ruby Tuesday Books Limited 2009

ACKNOWLEDGEMENTS

With thanks to Lorraine Petersen, Chief Executive of NASEN for her help in the development and creation of these books.

Images courtesy of Shutterstock; **front cover, pages 1, 3, 6, 8, 11, 19, 20, 21, 22, 26, 31, 32, 38-39, 43** Superstock

While every effort has been made to secure permission to use copyright material, the publishers apologise for any errors or omissions in the above list and would be grateful for notification of any corrections to be included in subsequent editions.

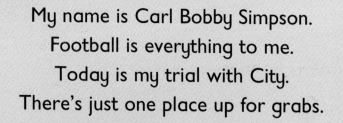

My name is Carl Bobby Simpson.
Football is everything to me.
Today is my trial with City.
There's just one place up for grabs.

THE LEARNING CENTRES
ACC No. R48796
DATE 22/01/10
CLASS FIC.PHI

GOAL

ONE MOMENT CAN CHANGE YOUR LIFE FOREVER

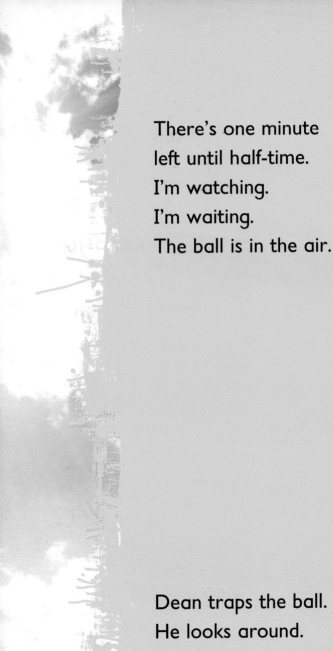

There's one minute
left until half-time.
I'm watching.
I'm waiting.
The ball is in the air.

Dean traps the ball.
He looks around.

I'm clear.

I shout, "Over here!"

But Dean's going for it.
He wants a goal.

The little defender comes up fast.
I shout to Dean, "Over here."

But Dean's left it too late.
The little defender tackles him.
The ball flies off the pitch.

It's half-time.
I run over to Mum in the small crowd.
She says, "You look good out there."
But I'm not happy. I want a goal.

Mum says, "Remember what Grandad used to say. Don't be a glory boy, Carl."

But today is my trial with City. Today, I need glory!

I was born the day after
Bobby Moore died.
My middle name is Bobby!

Carl and Grandad

Bobby Moore was Grandad's hero. He had a photo of Bobby lifting the World Cup.

"I'll watch you do that one day, Carl," Grandad used to say.

Football was everything in our house.
I played for my school.
I played in the league.

I never missed a game.
I never missed training.
"Work hard and play fair,"
Grandad used to say.

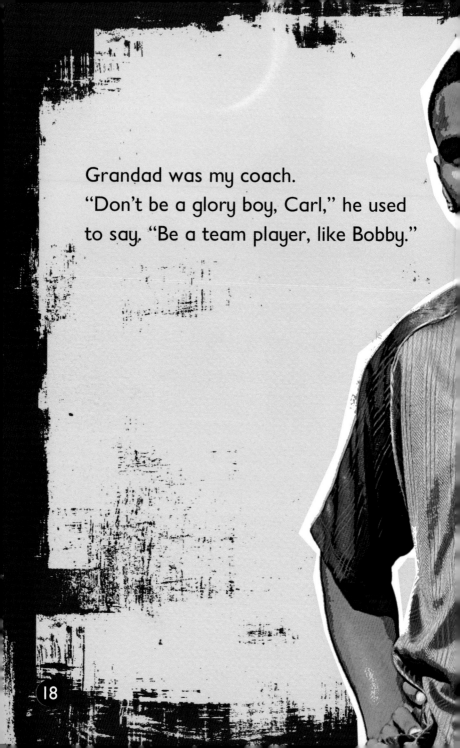

Grandad was my coach.
"Don't be a glory boy, Carl," he used
to say. "Be a team player, like Bobby."

But Bobby Moore was a defender.
I'm a forward — I need to score goals!

We're off again!
I jump for the ball.
The little defender's on me now.

I'm running with the ball.
I slow up.
I fake.
I look around.
Dean is to my right.
But I'm so close to the goal!

I'm off again.
But the defence is closing me down.

Dean is clear.
He can make it happen.
I cross.

Everyone looks at Dean.
Dean shoots!
It's a great goal.
But it's not my goal.

Last October, Grandad
told me he was ill.

I didn't believe him.

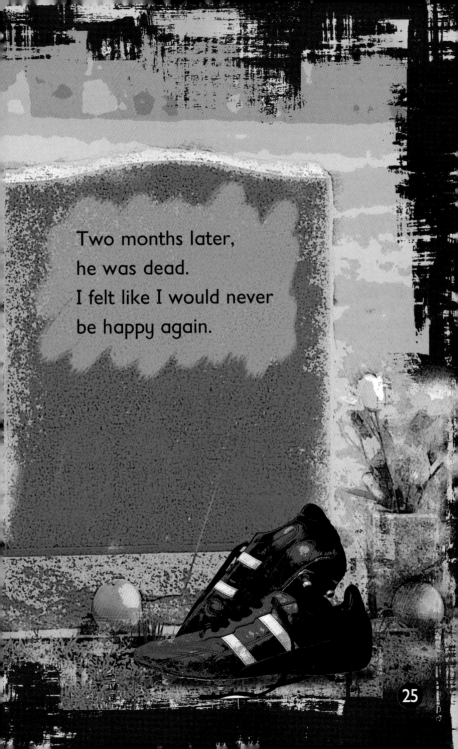

Two months later,
he was dead.
I felt like I would never
be happy again.

In January, we got the phone call.
I had a trial with City!
I felt happy and sad at the same time.

Dean got a trial, too.
But they only want one forward.
There's just one place up for grabs.

The whistle blows.
The tall guy passes to Dean.
Dean moves fast but that defender
is on him again. Dean swears.

Then,
SMACK!

The defender is rolling on the ground.

Dean boots the ball into the back of the net. Another goal.

I run to the defender and help him up.
He spits blood all over my shirt.
This is all going so wrong.

A medic takes the defender off.
I'm running again.
There's one minute left.
I pass to Dean.

Dean passes back.
I wave the tall guy forward.
I shout, "Dean, get left."

The goalie is right on top of me.
I pass to the tall guy.

Beautiful!

He crosses to Dean.

Textbook!

Suddenly, I forget this is a trial.
I forget the glory.
I forget everything.
We're making a goal.
Dean scores!

Beautiful!

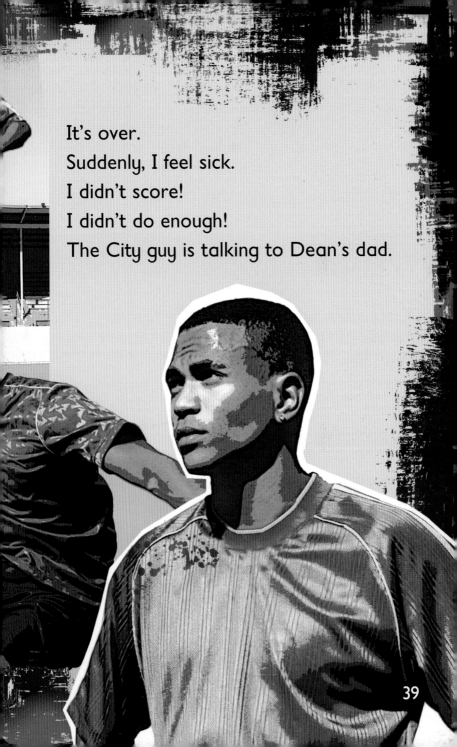

It's over.
Suddenly, I feel sick.
I didn't score!
I didn't do enough!
The City guy is talking to Dean's dad.

The City guy walks over to me.
He says, "You worked hard out
there, Carl. You're a leader."
I can see Mum smiling.

The City guy says, "We want
you to play for us, Carl."

The City guy smiles at me.

He says, "You're a team player Carl – we don't need glory boys."

GOAL - WHAT'S NEXT?

ROLE MODEL
ON YOUR OWN

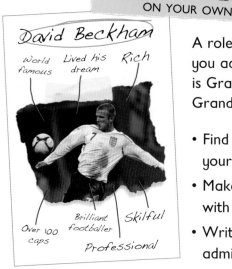

David Beckham

World famous • Lived his dream • Rich

Over 100 caps • Brilliant footballer • Skilful • Professional

A role model is somebody you admire. Bobby Moore is Grandad's role model. Grandad is Carl's role model!

- Find or draw a picture of your role model.
- Make a spider diagram with the picture in the middle.
- Write reasons why you admire your role model.

AFTER THE TRIAL
WITH A PARTNER

Role-play Dean and Carl being interviewed after the trial for a local news programme.

- Think about the questions the reporter will ask.
- Think about the answers that Dean and Carl will give.
- Role-play the interviews a few times, taking different roles.

LET'S TALK
IN A GROUP

The City guy tells Carl, "You're a leader." Then he says, "You're a team player."

In a group, discuss:

- How is it possible to be a leader and a team player at the same time?
- Why did the City guy choose Carl — even though Dean scored all the goals?

IT'S A GOAL!
ON YOUR OWN / WITH A PARTNER / IN A GROUP

Listen to a football commentator on the radio. There are no pictures — the words have to bring the match to life.

- Record a radio football commentary for pages 32 to 37. It must be accurate, exciting and to the point. All this action takes place in the last minute of the match!

IF YOU ENJOYED THIS BOOK, TRY THESE OTHER **RiGHT NOW!** BOOKS.

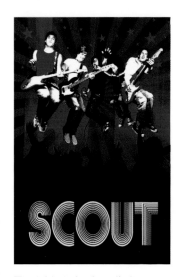

Tonight is the band's big chance. Tonight, a record company scout is at their gig!

Tonight, Vicky must make a choice. Stay in London with her boyfriend Chris. Or start a new life in Australia.

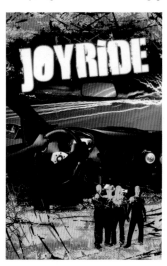

Dan sees the red car. The keys are inside. Dan says to Andy, Sam and Jess, "Want to go for a drive?"

It's Saturday night.
Two angry guys. Two knives.
There's going to be a fight.

Sophie hates this new town.
She misses her friends.
There's nowhere to skate!

Ed's platoon is under attack.
Another soldier is in danger.
Ed must risk his own life to
save him.

It's just an old, empty house.
Lauren must spend the night
inside. Just Lauren and the
ghost...